'This Book is a Cracker!'

- My Bum

ISBN 978-0-646-81936-5

THE WORLD'S #1 TALKING BUM

Scooby Baker

Chapter

HOW IT ALL ~~ST~~ARTED

I'll never forget the day my bum started talking. Well, I'd heard from it before, but just the usual sounds. Fppfft, Faarrrt, Rrripppp.

The sounds you usually hear when you go to the toilet. Sounds you would normally try to keep quiet, especially around the Christmas Dinner table or while spending time with Grandma.

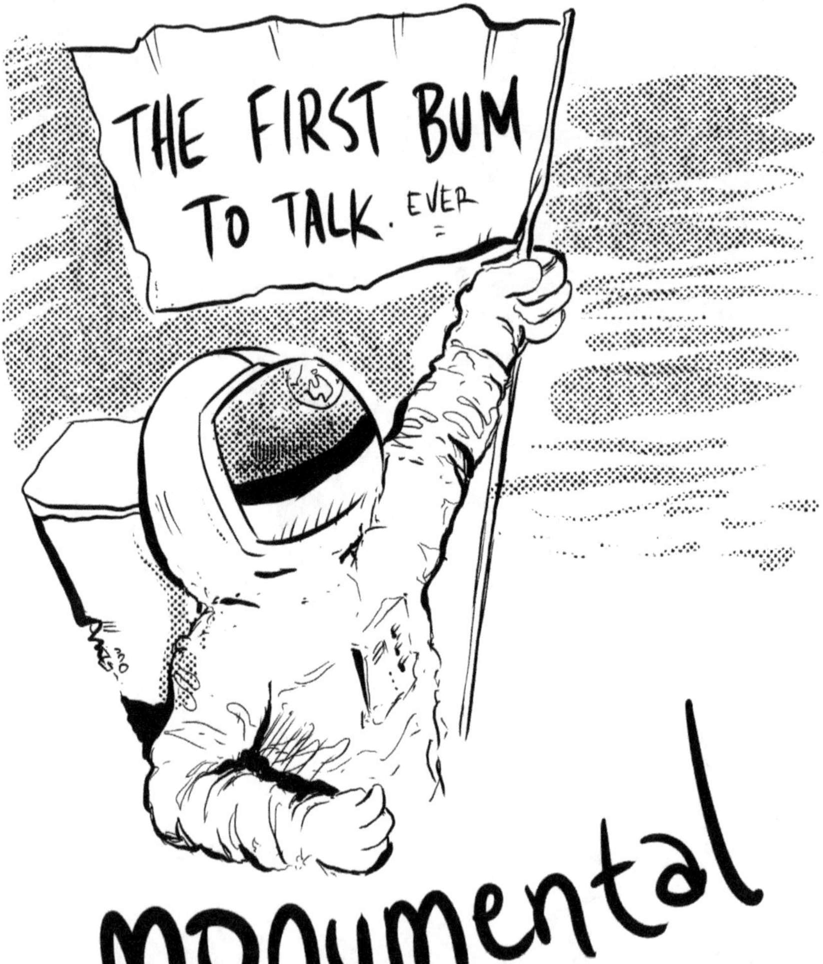

monumental time

No, this time it was different. This time my bum clearly said something. It was a monumental time.

Kind of like when man first set foot on the moon. Things would never be the same.

But my butt didn't say anything profound the first time it spoke. In fact, what my butt said was quite short and sweet. Actually, I shouldn't say it was sweet as it was rather rude. That's right, my butt had an attitude or should I say a 'Butt-itude.'

Not only that, but my bum spat out what it said with a fierce smell. A smell worse than one of Dad's ones after a night eating hot chilli nachos with extra cabbage topped with Mexican baked beans.

Have you ever smelt someone with bad breath? Well, my butt had the type of breath that no mint could fix.

My name is Dale, but my friends now call me Scooby. By this stage you are probably wondering what my bum first said.

Well... it wasn't nice.

Chapter

FIRST WORDS FROM BELOW

So, you have made it to Chapter 2. You must really want to find out what my bum said. Are you sure? Do you really want to read a book about my talking bum?
Wouldn't you rather listen to what your parents or your teacher has to say than my butt? No? Well, that's not saying much for them!

Okay, you win, but I warn you that once you start reading what my butt had to say, it is hard to stop if you know what I mean.

Alright, I was laying on the loungeroom floor watching the box when I heard a muffled sound. It was hard to hear at first as I was eating some snacks.

I wasn't even letting one go. I can let them rip like the best of the them, but I can assure you that my bum spoke without me having to let any wind out of the chamber, if you know what I mean?

The first muffled and grumbly words I heard my bum say were...

'For Butt's Sake... stop eating those.'

Startled I jumped up and asked, 'Who said that?' At first, I thought it was a ghost or someone playing tricks on me, but then it replied.

'It's me' 'Your crack in your dacks'
'Your butt cushion'
'The cheeks your mum doesn't kiss'

I twisted myself around and sure enough the voice was coming from my backside. 'Stop eating those' it grumbled, 'You're going to make me sick'. 'What? but how?' I asked. 'By eating too much of that junky rubbish' it groaned. 'No, how is my bum talking. How did this happen? What is happening to me?' I thought.

My bum reminded me that a week ago, I was a little cheeky to an old Gypsy Lady at the local show. I was walking by someone getting their fortune told and in passing I grumbled... 'Yeah, yeah, keep talking that rubbish.'

18

Little did I know that while I was walking away she had placed a spell on my butt to *start* talking.

I started to panic. What was I going to do? Who could I tell?

'Settle down Worry-Wort, this isn't the end of the world' my butt mumbled, 'I can help you, but you can't flip out every time you hear my voice, you must trust me, and you must stop eating that junk.

'Are you picking up what I putting down?'

'Are you mowing what I'm growing?'

'Are you smellin' what I'm cookin?'

ARE YOU PICKING UP WHAT I'M PUTTING DOWN?
ARE YOU MOWING WHAT I'M GROWING?
ARE YOU SMELLING WHAT I'M COOKIN'?

'Deal?' It asked

'Deal' I reluctantly sighed.

Oh great, now I'm making deals
with my bum, I thought.

Chapter

3

SOCIAL
'BUTT'ERFLY

The next day I was at school hoping that my bum wouldn't start talking to other people. At this stage, it had only spoken to me. This didn't last long.

My bum started to say hello to people as I walked to class. I pretended that it was me saying hello, as how was I meant to explain?

The trouble was that my bum started saying things that I don't normally say.

Sayings like... 'Hey Little Dude!' and 'Stay Fresh Cheese Bags.'

'Whadddup Bro!' 'Catch you on da Flip' it continued. My bum was enjoying calling out to people, but if this kept up people would start to think that I had a different personality.

I quickly walked into the classroom and sat on my chair hoping that it would keep my bum quiet.

I didn't want my friends to know. I didn't want my teacher to know. And I sure didn't want Jessica to know.

Jessica, or 'Jess' and I had been friends since Kinder. I liked her heaps and I think she liked me. If she found out, well… I'd just die.

I sat hard down into my seat, pushing my bum down as to ensure silence from the

below the equator. But it didn't last long.

Chapter

4

CRACKING
THE ICE

Oh no! Jess was coming into the classroom. I squeezed my butt-cheeks together, but out it came…

'*Well, Heeeelllllo Baby Girl!* screeched out my butt to Jess.

Embarrassed, I pretended someone else in the classroom had said it.

I ran out of the classroom, motioning to my teacher that I needed to go to the bathroom. Ekk! I hope no-one noticed.

In the toilet cubical I tried to reason with my bum. 'We have to work together' I pleaded.

'True That' my bum blurted. 'If you want that pretty sweet baby girl to fall for you…leave it to me!'

'I've got just the thing' it said.

'I call it the 'Ita Buttrose' move.

She'll love it!'

'OH. MY. GOD. NO!' I screamed.
'You've got Poo for Brains' I shouted,
which was kind of true. What was I
going to do?

That's it! I remembered that my bum
didn't like me eating 'junky food' so I
threatened I would again if it said
anything to Jess. My bum
finally agreed with me and we went
back to class.

Things got back to normal and by
the afternoon my teacher started
teaching us about the planets as she
normally did on Tuesday afternoons.
We had already learnt about Pluto,
Mars and Neptune and today she
announced that we were to learn
about Uranus.

A sound of laughter rang around the classroom. All the kids laughed whenever she said the word 'Uranus.' 'That's enough laughing' she demanded, trying to calm the class down. I was laughing too until I felt my bum having a laugh as well. Uh-oh … not again.

I tried again to sit firmly in my chair. The lesson went on. All was going okay until my teacher asked students to call out some facts they knew about Uranus. I could feel my butt bursting to yell out. I held it and held it until I couldn't anymore.

'You're Uranus is HUUUGGGE Mrs Cracknell!' yelled out my bum. The class burst out in laughter.

At the time, I had to move my mouth as if I was saying it as I didn't want everyone to know it was my bum. 'Not only that Mrs Cracknell, but Uranus is also sooo COOOOLD! Uranus is HUGE, Freezing Cold and really Gassy!'

The kids started falling off their chairs laughing. Some kids were crying with laughter. I think Billy may have laughed so much that he pee'ed his pants.

Jess looked at me wondering why I was saying such things, but I couldn't tell her. Mrs Cracknell wasn't impressed. Her face went red, her glasses fogged over, and she yelled back at me to leave the classroom straight away.

 She organised a meeting with my parents that night to discuss the matter. Awesome. Now my bum had me in huge trouble.

Chapter

5

THE
MEETING

My parents were shocked that I had caused so much trouble. Dad wasn't impressed, and Mum was embarrassed about what my butt had said.

Now we were all sitting in Mrs Cracknell's office about to run through the whole thing again. It was first time I had been in real trouble at school and I didn't like it one bit.

I sat between Mum and Dad, who sat in silence looking around the room as Mrs Cracknell fished out my student file from her drawer. She had already told them over the phone what had happened so the car ride back to school with my parents for this meeting was frosty to say the least.

Mrs Cracknell started reading out the events as my parents listened, sighing in disapproval. Dad crossed his arms and shook his head. I could tell Mum was getting embarrassed as her eyes started blinking, which is what happens when she feels uncomfortable.

'So young Dale, what have you got to say for yourself?' Mrs Cracknell snapped What was I meant to say?

Maybe I should just tell them about the spell the Gypsy Lady had placed on me, I thought? Why not, my butt hadn't said anything to try and help me out of this pickle. Just as I was about to 'spill the beans' I felt a force in my bum. It was about to speak and speak it did.

'It was ME! The mouth from the south.
The crack in his dacks.

The air leak from his bare cheeks!'

Astonished, my parents and teacher jumped up in surprise. That is amazing! How are you doing that? They cried.

And it was on. My butt seemed to talk forever to them. It told them the story of the Gypsy Lady and how it came to be that my bum could talk.

Amazingly I wasn't in trouble any more. In fact, their attention changed from me to my talking bum and the Gypsy Lady. Mrs Cracknell wasn't impressed at all with her. How could someone do this to an innocent kid? We must go back to her this weekend! She declared.

The town fair only runs for one more weekend, she explained. "We must see her, get this curse lifted and give her a piece of my mind!'

Mrs Cracknell was on a war path!

YOU STICK WITH ME. ERR... WHAT WAS THAT?
NOTHING!
FARTASTIC!
Meeting Notes
Dale's buttocks talks due to Gypsy Lady at local fair
Action: Must visit this weekend to rectify.
P.S. Buy more pencils.
Mrs. Crackwell.

'But that is two days away' I said. 'How am I going to get through two more days of school if my butt keeps talking?

Don't worry Dale. We have the school talent day on Thursday and Athletics day on Friday. The other kids will be distracted with all the other goings on. You stick close to me and all will be fine.

'Oh great' I thought. Now I must hang around Mrs Cracknell with my talking bum.

Chapter

6

TALENT QUEST

The next day was the school Talent Quest. Some kids had been practising their acts for weeks. I normally enjoyed this day, but this year I had to stick with Mrs Cracknell. She explained to the kids in my class that as I had been yelling out inappropriately the day before, I would need to be close to her all day so she could keep an eye on me. I wasn't sure this was a good idea.

The school had invited a guest judge for the day, Slim Jim and his dog Dusty. Slim Jim played guitar while his dog danced. They were once on a TV talent show a few years ago. They weren't really celebrities, but anytime the school got anyone semi famous in the kids went nuts. Mrs C was right, everyone was too distracted to notice my butt troubles.

The day ran smoothly. Kids performed act after act. Some juggled tennis balls, some told jokes, other danced together to popular songs. Slim Jim and his dog

Dusty performed at the interval.

All the while I had to sit with Mrs C at the back of the school hall. She was keeping an eye on me the whole time and then she noticed that there was still some time to fill. School still had at least an hour to go and as there were some act cancellations, she was starting to panic.

Suddenly Mrs C had an idea. 'A-ha..I know!' she said excitedly as she pulled a sock out of her handbag. I wasn't sure what she was thinking as she drew two dots on the sock with a thick black texta, but then it dawned on me. She was wanting me to go up on stage and do a ventriloquist act.

She slipped the sock on my hand. 'No way!' I said, 'I can't do it. I can't control what my butt says.'

You'll be right' she replied. 'The kids will love it.'

Before I knew it, Mrs C was ushering me to the stage announcing that we had one last talent act. My butt started bulging and I could tell that it was ready to take centre stage.

Nervously, I stood there looking down to all the kids in my school. I could see everyone. My friends, my enemies, the lot. I could even see Jess staring at me from the corner of the room. The Hall went silent and I had no idea what to say.

I had to begin somehow…

'H-H-Hello' I nervously stuttered into the microphone. "My name is Dale, and this here is my Friend Socko' introducing the sock on my hand to the crowd.

I opened and closed my hand pretending that the sock was talking.

'Socko!' Yelled out my Butt, 'What type of name is that?'

The kids laughed.

'I don't know', I replied, 'what name do you want?'

'Principal Butt-face' yelled my butt.

The kids roared with laughter. 'I rule this School' it said, 'Don't I kids?'

'YEEEEEEEAAAhhhh!' all the kids excitingly yelled back.

The whole school was in the palm of my hand, which was being controlled by my butt.

Nothing was out of limits. Principal Butt-Face told jokes, did funny impressions of the teachers and finished with a rendition of the alphabet in fart sounds.

Slim Jim and his dog Dusty were blown away. We got a standing ovation and won the talent quest. The first prize was One Hundred Dollars.

This was the best day of my life.

Mrs C stood at the back of the hall proudly clapping. Her sock idea had worked.

Chapter

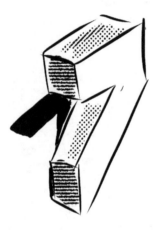

ATHS
DAY

That day had been my best day of my life so far! No day could top that, or so I thought. All the kids had loved my sock act so while getting dressed for school the next day, Aths Day, I figured I'd wear the 'Principal Butt-face' sock on my hand. That way if my butt started talking to people I could blame it on him.

Now I am not a gifted athlete, so I wasn't particularly looking forward to this day. Our School House Colour hadn't won since I was in grade 1.

As any kid knows, there is a bit of waiting around on Aths days. And when I say, 'a bit' I mean a LOT. Waiting for events, waiting while lining up, waiting for lunchtime.

The only kids that love Aths Day are those thay can run, jump and throw

further, longer and faster than others.

Early that morning Mrs C checked in with me to see how I was going. She could see that I had worn the sock and was happy for me to join in with the other kids knowing that I had 'Principal Butt-face' to deflect any unwanted attention from my bum.

It was a hot day and my first event was high jump. I wish I could say that I could jump as high as my height, but I couldn't. Or at least I couldn't before this day.

It was my turn to jump. I did my normal nervous run up to the high jump pole hoping not to injure myself and as I jumped up my bum yelled out a huge 'Boooooooo-Yahhhhhhhhh.'

The sudden gust of air from my backdoor had lifted me up high and over the pole. I had done it! I lifted 'Principal Butt-Face' to the sky in celebration.

The kids in my house colour all cheered.

This was awesome. I had never won high jump before. Everything was working out for me. Or so I thought.

'Give me that!' growled Boris as he yanked the sock from my hand. Boris was a Boof-head. All the teachers knew it, but couldn't say it, and all the kids knew it too.

It was really Boris' fault that day at the fair a week ago when I said something to that Gypsy Lady. I was trying to win a teddy for Jess when he put me off just before I was about to win. He was the one that put me in a bad mood.
'Let's see how you go now' without this thing' he said holding Principal Butthead up in the air, so I couldn't reach it.

My butt started to bulge. It was ready to let Boris cop a yelling from my mouth from the south. I felt the urge to turn my butt towards him and let it rip, but held back as I was set to race him in the next

100 metre sprint event.

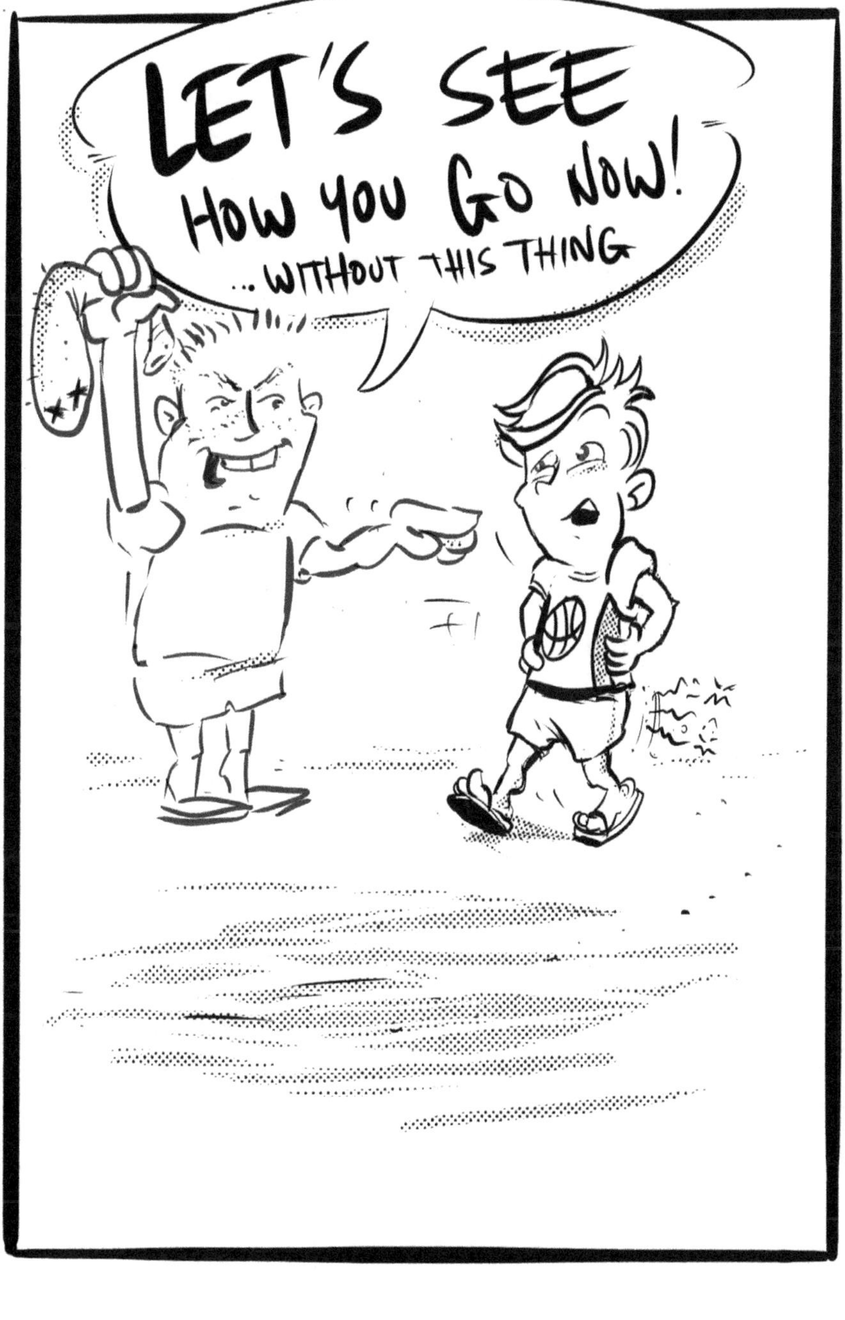
LET'S SEE
HOW YOU GO NOW!
...WITHOUT THIS THING

While waiting for my turn to race, my stomach gurgled. It was eager to give Boris 'a piece of its mind', as Mrs C would say. We lined up at the starting line and I was as nervous as I had ever been.   Ready, Set… Go!

We were off. Boris had jumped the start and had gotten off into a good lead. My legs were running as fast as they could. The kids on the side were screaming and cheering. They didn't want Boris to win either. As I strained and strained I must have pushed something into gear. Turbo gear.

I farted so hard and fast that it pushed my waist forward and propelled me closer to Boris. I tried it again, this time farting so loud that houses neighbouring the school would have heard it if it wasn't for the cheering of all the kids.

The second fart had pushed me level with Boris. In my mind I heard the Chariots of Fire theme song as I let one last huge one rip. It was a rip-snorter. I crossed the line in first place leaving Boris for dead in the smell of sweet, sweet revenge.*

*Not sweet at all. Rather smelly.

Boris collapsed in a heap before the finish line. The kids cheered as I swiped back Principal Butt-face placing him back on my hand as I lifted him in the air!

All the kids roared and cheered, even Jess.

It had to be the second best day of my life!

Chapter

GYPSY
LADY

The next day was Saturday. I was starting to dread going back to see the Gypsy Lady for two reasons. 1. I didn't really want to talk with an old Lady who casts spells on kids and 2. I was starting to like having a butt that talks. With the help of my butt, I had gone from a quiet mannered and somewhat shy kid to one of the most popular kids in school!

Remember at the start of the book I mentioned that only my friends called me Scoob? That was only 3 kids, but now everyone called me it. Everyone wanted to be my friend. I was even starting to talk in my bum's lingo. Are you snackin' what I'm packin'?

For a minute I thought of darting off on my BMX so my parents and Mrs C couldn't take me to the Fair, but it suddenly dawned on me that I had $100 and started dreaming of all the rides and showbags I could buy with it. I was going.

Mrs C picked us up in her car. It was an old bomb. Teachers don't get paid as much as they should I thought. It had taken a while, but I was starting to warm to her. Without Mrs C's brilliant idea of the using the sock to deflect

attention, things could have been terrible.

We arrived at 9.30am. Some of the stallholders were still setting up for the day. My Dad asked around if anyone had seen the Old Gypsy Lady. 'There she is!' shouted Mrs C as she rushed in her direction. Mum, Dad and I followed as I looked longingly at all the rides and showbags.

The Old Gypsy lady was staring into her crystal ball as Mrs C stormed up her with a determined and stern frown on her face. 'Can I help you?' asked the Gypsy Lady raising her head from the gaze of the crystal ball.

'How dare you' yelled Mr C. 'How dare you place a spell on an innocent young child' she continued as she gestured to me and my butt. By this stage the Old Gypsy had realised that I was the boy that had given her a cheeky passing re-

mark the week before.

'Perhaps this young boy would like to say sorry for his words to me' she replied. 'Words can be powerful. Words can be kind, but without using them correctly my help you will not find.'

My parents gestured for me to apologise, as did Mrs C. 'I'm sorry' I relented.

The Old Gypsy Lady noddled in approval. 'One more thing before you go, I will need $100 for your butt talking to go'.

'$100!' Mrs C snapped 'That is a rip-off! You should be ashamed of yourself making money that way!' Mrs C was furious and had heard enough. She turned away in disgust mumbling something under her breath.

'Your teacher should also watch her mouth as she does not know everything.' 'In fact, she might now have something down south that can also talk and sing'.

The Gypsy placed out her hand gesturing that I pay up. Mum and Dad nodded. I had so many plans for the $100. In particular, Show-bags and rides. I handed over the money and felt an instant relief. Mum and Dad gave me a reassuring hug and with that the spirt of my talking bum had left my body.

I looked over my parents' shoulders to see Mrs C in the distance snacking on a Dagwood Dog on a Stick.

It reminded me that my bum didn't like me eating food like that. Something told me that Mrs. C was just about to learn that herself.

I brought Principal Butt-Face in for her on that next Monday. I think she needed it at the Morning Staff Meeting. I would have loved to hear what went down at that meeting!

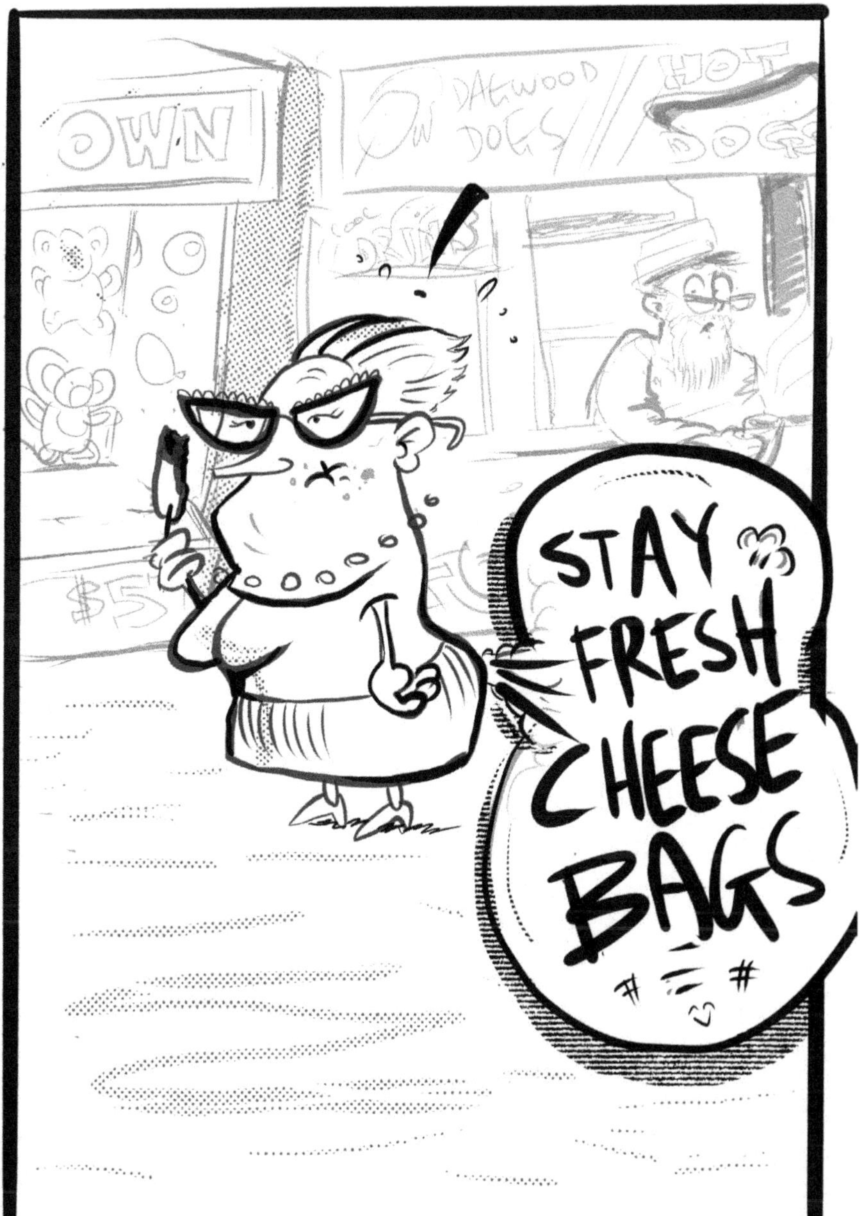
OWN
DAGWOOD DOGS
HOT DOGS
STAY FRESH CHEESE BAGS